Strawberry Fair

51 traditional songs

MELODY EDITION

A&C Black · London

Strawberry Fair

Songs chosen by Sue Williams
Cover by Tessa Barwick
Illustrations by Chris Rothero

First published 1985
by A & C Black (Publishers) Ltd,
35 Bedford Row, London WC1R 4JH
© 1985 A & C Black (Publishers) Ltd

ISBN 0-7136-2677-1

Printed in Great Britain by
Hollen Street Press Ltd, Slough, Berkshire.

Contents

1 Mairi's wedding

traditional Gaelic

Chorus

Step we gai-ly, on we go, Heel for heel and toe for toe,—

Arm in arm and row on row, All for Mai-ri's wed - ding.

1. O - ver hill - ways up and down, Myr - tle green and bracken brown,

Past the sheil-ings, through the town, All for sake of Mai - ri.

2 Red her cheeks as rowans are,
   Bright her eye as any star,
   Fairest of them all by far,
   Is our darling Mairi.
        Step we gaily, on we go . . .

3 Plenty herring, plenty meal,
   Plenty peat to fill her creel,
   Plenty bonnie bairns as weel;
   That's the toast for Mairi.
        Step we gaily, on we go . . .

sheiling: summer pasture on a hillside
creel: basket

2 Oh soldier, soldier

traditional English

1. "Oh sold-ier, sold-ier won't you marry me With your mus-ket, fife and drum?" "Oh no, sweet maid, I cannot marry thee, For I have no coat to put
2. hat
3. gloves
4. boots

on." Then up she went to her grand-father's chest And got him a coat of the
2. hat
3. pair
4. pair

ver-y, ver-y best, She got him a coat of the ver-y, ver-y best, And the sold-ier put it____
2. hat 2. it____
3. pair 3. them
4. pair 4. them

on. "Oh on. "Oh sold-ier, sold-ier won't you marry me With your musk-et, fife and

drum?" "Oh no, sweet maid, I can-not marry thee, For I have a wife of my own."

3 The Lincolnshire Poacher

traditional English

1. When I was bound ap - pren - tice in fa - mous Lin - coln -

-shire, Full well I served my ma - ster for

more than se - ven year, Till I took up to poach - ing, as

you shall quick - ly hear; **Chorus** Oh! 'tis my de - light on a

shin - ing night in the sea - son of the year, Oh! 'tis

my de-light on a shin - ing night in the sea - son of the year.

2   As me and my companions were setting of a snare,
    'Twas then we spied the gamekeeper, for him we did not care.
    For we can wrestle and fight, my boys, and jump out anywhere;
        Oh! 'tis my delight on a shining night . . .

3   As me and my companions were setting four or five,
    And taking of them up again, we caught a hare alive;
    We caught a hare alive, my boys, and through the woods did steer;
        Oh! 'tis my delight on a shining night . . .

4   I took him on my shoulder, and then we trudgèd home,
    We took him to a neighbour's house and sold him for a crown;
    We sold him for a crown, my boys, I did not tell you where;
        Oh! 'tis my delight on a shining night . . .

5   Success to every gentleman who lives in Lincolnshire,
    Success to every poacher who wants to sell a hare,
    Bad luck to every gamekeeper who will not sell his deer;
        Oh! 'tis my delight on a shining night . . .

4 Strawberry Fair

traditional English

As I was going to Straw-ber-ry Fair, Ri - fol, ri - fol,

tol-de-rid-dle-li - do, I met a maid-en sel-ling her ware, Fol-de-dee. I

met a maid-en sel-ling her ware As she went on to Straw-ber-ry Fair,

Ri - fol, ri - fol, tol-de-riddle-li - do, Ri - fol, ri - fol, tol-de-rid-dle-dee.

5 Spinning wheel song

traditional Manx

1. Spin, wheel,— spin, Turn, wheel,— turn, And

ev - 'ry leaf up - on the trees Spin a - bove my head.

Chorus

With my - self, the spin - ner, And spin-ning the grey wool,

Help me get my spin-ning done Be - fore the weav - er come.

2 Spin, wheel, spin,
   Sing, wheel, sing,
   And ev'ry slate upon the house
   Spin on my behalf.
        With myself, the spinner . . .

3 Spin, wheel, spin,
   Hum, wheel, hum,
   And ev'ry wave along the shore
   Spin along with me.
        With myself, the spinner . . .

6 Cockles and mussels

traditional Irish

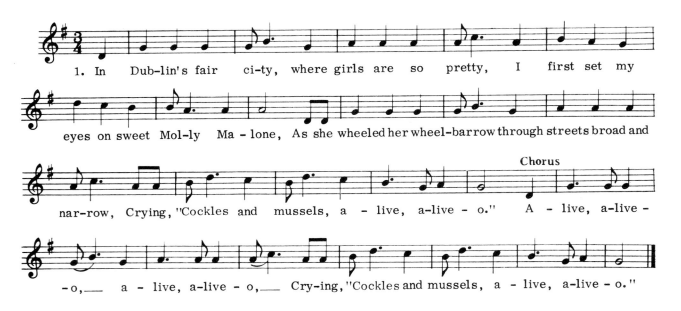

1. In Dub-lin's fair ci-ty, where girls are so pretty, I first set my eyes on sweet Mol-ly Ma - lone, As she wheeled her wheel-barrow through streets broad and nar-row, Crying, "Cockles and mussels, a - live, a-live - o."

Chorus

A - live, a-live - o, — a - live, a-live - o, — Cry-ing, "Cockles and mussels, a - live, a-live - o."

2 She was a fishmonger, but sure 'twas no wonder,
  For so were her mother and father before,
  And they each wheeled their barrow through streets broad and narrow,
  Crying, "Cockles and mussels, alive, alive-o."
   Alive, alive-o, alive, alive-o . . .

3 She died of a fever, and no one could save her,
  And that was the end of sweet Molly Malone,
  And her ghost wheeled her barrow through streets broad and narrow,
  Crying, "Cockles and mussels, alive, alive-o."
   Alive, alive-o, alive, alive-o . . .

7 A-Roving

traditional (capstan shanty)

1. In Am - ster - dam there lived a maid, Mark well what I do say. In Am - ster - dam there lived a maid And she was mis - tress of her trade

Chorus I'll go no more a - ro - ving with you fair maid, A - ro - ving, a - ro - ving, since ro-ving's been my *ru - (i) - in, I'll go no more a - ro - ving with you fair maid.

2 Her cheeks were red, her eyes were brown,
   Mark well what I do say.
   Her cheeks were red, her eyes were brown,
   Her hair so black was hanging down.
      I'll go no more a-roving . . .

3 I put my arm around her waist,
   Mark well what I do say.
   I put my arm around her waist,
   Says she, "Young man, you're in great haste!"
      I'll go no more a-roving . . .

★pronounced "roo-eye-in"

8 Billy Boy

Northumbrian shanty

1. Where have ye been all the day, Bil - ly Boy, Bil - ly Boy? Where have ye been all the day, me Bil - ly Boy? I've been walk - in' all the day With me char - min' Nan - cy Grey. And me Nan - cy kit - t'ld me fan - cy Oh, me char - min' Bil - ly Boy.

Chorus

2   Is she fit to be your wife,
      Billy Boy, Billy Boy?
   Is she fit to be your wife.
      me Billy Boy?
   She's as fit to be me wife
   As the fork is to the knife.
        And me Nancy kittl'd me fancy . . .

3   Can she cook a bit o'steak,
      Billy Boy, Billy Boy?
   Can she cook a bit o'steak,
      me Billy Boy?
   She can cook a bit o' steak,
   Aye, and make a girdle cake.
        And me Nancy kittl'd me fancy . . .

4   Can she make an Irish stew,
      Billy Boy, Billy Boy?
   Can she make an Irish stew,
      me Billy Boy?
   She can make an Irish stew,
   Aye, and "Singin' Hinnies" too.
        And me Nancy kittl'd me fancy . . .

kittl'd: tickled
girdle cake: cake baked on a griddle
Singin' Hinnies: a type of large teacake, usually
abundantly covered with currants

9 Dashing away with the smoothing iron

traditional English

1. 'Twas on a Mon - day morn - ing When I be - held my dar - ling, She looked so neat and charm - ing In ev - ery high de - gree; She looked so neat and nim - ble, O A - wash - ing of her li - nen, O

Chorus

Dash - ing a - way with the smooth - ing iron, Dash - ing a - way with the smooth - ing iron She stole my heart a - way.

2 'Twas on a Tuesday morning
When I beheld my darling,
She looked so neat and charming
In every high degree;
She looked so neat and nimble, O
A-hanging out her linen, O
    Dashing away with the smoothing iron . . .

3 'Twas on a Wednesday morning
When I beheld my darling,
She looked so neat and charming
In every high degree;
She looked so neat and nimble, O
A-starching of her linen, O
    Dashing away with the smoothing iron . . .

4 'Twas on a Thursday morning
When I beheld my darling,
She looked so neat and charming
In every high degree;
She looked so neat and nimble, O
A-ironing of her linen, O
    Dashing away with the smoothing iron . . .

5 'Twas on a Friday morning
When I beheld my darling,
She looked so neat and charming
In every high degree;
She looked so neat and nimble, O
A-folding of her linen, O
    Dashing away with the smoothing iron . . .

6 'Twas on a Saturday morning
When I beheld my darling,
She looked so neat and charming
In every high degree;
She looked so neat and nimble, O
A-airing of her linen, O
    Dashing away with the smoothing iron . . .

7 'Twas on a Sunday morning
When I beheld my darling,
She looked so neat and charming
In every high degree;
She looked so neat and nimble, O
A-wearing of her linen, O
    Dashing away with the smoothing iron . . .

10 Loch Lomond

traditional Scottish

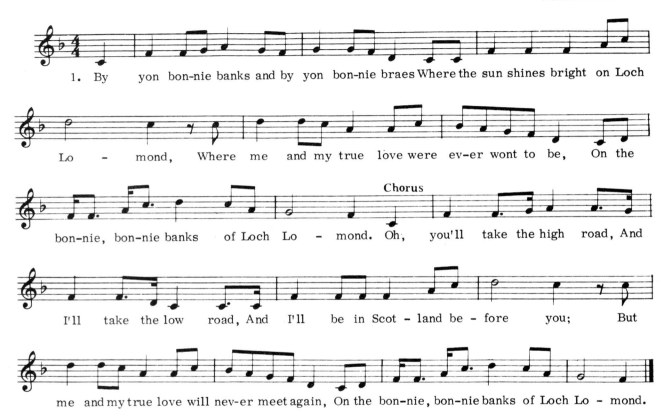

1. By yon bon-nie banks and by yon bon-nie braes Where the sun shines bright on Loch Lo - mond, Where me and my true love were ev-er wont to be, On the bon-nie, bon-nie banks of Loch Lo - mond.

Chorus

Oh, you'll take the high road, And I'll take the low road, And I'll be in Scot - land be - fore you; But me and my true love will nev-er meet again, On the bon-nie, bon-nie banks of Loch Lo - mond.

2 'Twas there that we parted in yon shady glen
On the steep, steep side of Ben Lomond,
Where in purple hue the Highland hills we view,
And the moon coming out in the gloaming.
    Oh, you'll take the high road . . .

brae: slope or hillside

11 The Miller of Dee

traditional English

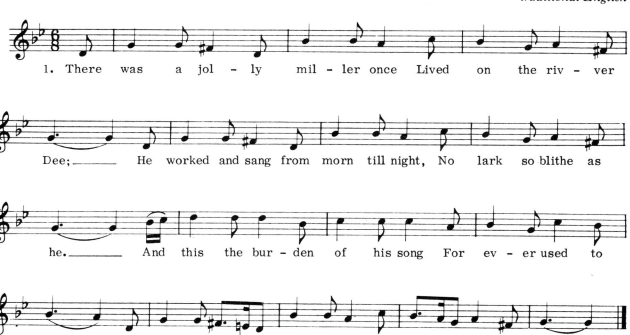

1. There was a jol-ly mil-ler once Lived on the riv-ver Dee;____ He worked and sang from morn till night, No lark so blithe as he.____ And this the bur-den of his song For ev-er used to be,____ "I care for no-bod-y, no, not I, If no-body cares for me."____

2   I live by my mill, she is to me
    Like parent, child and wife;
    I would not change my station
    For any other in life.
    No lawyer, surgeon or doctor
    E'er had a groat from me.
    I care for nobody, no, not I,
    If nobody cares for me."

12 The Keeper

traditional English

1. The Keep-er did a-shoot-ing go, And un-der his cloak he carried a bow,

All for to shoot at a mer-ry lit-tle doe A-mong the leaves so___ green - o.

Chorus (singers divide into two groups)

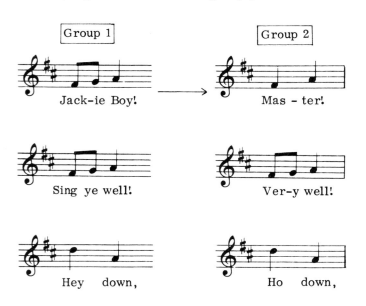

Group 1 — Jack-ie Boy!

Group 2 — Mas - ter!

Sing ye well!

Ver-y well!

Hey down,

Ho down,

Der-ry der-ry down,

A - mong the leaves so＿ green - o.

To my hey down down,

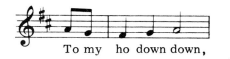

To my ho down down,

Hey down,

Ho down,

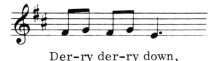

Der-ry der-ry down,

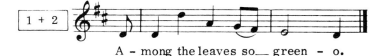

A - mong the leaves so＿ green - o.

2 The first doe he shot at he missed,
The second doe he trimmed he kissed,
The third doe went where nobody wist
Among the leaves so green-o.
        Jackie Boy!   Master! . . .

3 The fourth doe she did cross the plain;
The Keeper fetched her back again.
Where she is now she may remain
Among the leaves so green-o.
        Jackie Boy!   Master! . . .

4 The fifth doe she did cross the brook;
The Keeper fetched her back with his crook.
Where she is now you must go and look
Among the leaves so green-o.
        Jackie Boy!   Master! . . .

13 Brennan on the moor

traditional Irish

1. It's of a fear - less high - way - man a stor - y I will tell; His name was Bil-ly Bren — nan in Ire - land he did dwell. 'Twas on the Kil - worth moun - tains he com-menced his wild ca - -reer, Where man-y a wealth-y gen - tle - man be - fore him shook with fear,

Chorus

And it's Bren-nan on the moor, Bren-nan on the moor, So bold and un - daunt-ed stood Bill Bren-nan on the moor.

2   A brace of loaded pistols he carried night and day;
He never robbed a poor man upon the King's highway.
But what he'd taken from the rich, like Turpin and
   Black Bess,
He always would divide it with the widow in distress.
      And it's Brennan on the moor, Brennan on the moor . . .

3   One night he robbed a packman, his name was Pedlar Brown;
They travelled on together till day began to dawn.
The pedlar seeing his money gone, likewise his watch
   and chain,
He at once encountered Brennan and robbed them back again.
      And it's Brennan on the moor, Brennan on the moor . . .

4   When Brennan saw the pedlar was as good a man as he,
He took him on the highway, his companion for to be.
The pedlar threw away his pack without any more delay,
And proved a faithful comrade until his dying day.
      And it's Brennan on the moor, Brennan on the moor . . .

14 Blow the wind southerly

traditional English

1. Blow the wind south-er-ly, south-er-ly, south-er-ly, Blow the wind south o'er the
Blow the wind south-er-ly, south-er-ly, south-er-ly, Blow, bon-ny breeze, — my

bonny blue sea, lov-er to me. They told me last night there were ships in the of-fing, And

I hur-ried down to the deep rol-ling sea; But my eye could not see it, wher-

ev-er might be it, The bark that is bear-ing my lov-er to me.

2 Blow the wind southerly, southerly,
   southerly,
   Blow the wind south o'er the bonny
   blue sea.
   Blow the wind southerly, southerly,
   southerly,
   Blow, bonny breeze, and bring him to
   me.

Is it not sweet to hear the breeze
   sighing,
As lightly it comes o'er the deep
   rolling sea?
But sweeter and dearer by far when
   'tis bringing
The bark of my true love in safety
   to me.

15 Charlie is my darling

words: Lady Nairne
melody: traditional Scottish

Chorus
Char - lie is my dar - ling, my dar - ling, my dar - ling,

Fine
Char - lie is my dar - ling the young chev - a - lier.

Verse
1. 'Twas on a Mon-day morn - ing Right ear - ly in the year, When

D. C. al fine
Char - lie came to our town, the young chev - a - lier. Oh!

2 As he came marching up the street
The pipes played loud and clear,
And all the folks came running out
To meet the chevalier.
    Oh! Charlie is my darling . . .

3 They've left their bonnie Highland hills,
Their wives and children dear,
To draw the sword for Scotland's lord,
The young chevalier.
    Oh! Charlie is my darling . . .

4 Oh there were many beating hearts
And many a hope and fear;
And many were the prayers put up
For the young chevalier.
    Oh! Charlie is my darling . . .

16 Caller herrin'

words: *Lady Nairne*
melody: *traditional Scottish*

Chorus

Who'll buy cal — ler her — rin'? They're bon-nie fish and hale-some far-in';

Buy my cal — ler her — rin', New drawn— from the Forth.

Verse

1. When you were sleep-ing on your pil-lows, Dreamed you aught of our poor fel-lows,

Dark-ling as they faced the bil-lows, All to fill our wov-en wil-lows?

Chorus

Buy my cal — ler her — rin', They're bon-nie fish and hale-some fa-rin';

Buy my cal — ler her — rin', New drawn— from the Forth. Forth.

2 And when the creel of herrin' passes,
   Ladies clad in silks and laces,
   Gather in their braw pelisses,
   Toss their heads and screw their faces.
       Buy my caller herrin' . . .

3 Now, neighbour wives, come heed my tellin',
   When the bonnie fish you're sellin',
   At a word be aye your dealin',
   Truth will stand when a' things failin'.
       Buy my caller herrin' . . .

caller: short *a* (as in 'shall', not as in 'call'), meaning fresh
creel: basket
braw: smart

17 The tailor and the mouse

traditional English

1. There was a tail - or had a mouse, Hi did-dle un-kum

fee - dle. They lived to - geth - er in one house, Hi did-dle un-kum

Chorus

fee - dle. Hi did-dle un-kum ta - rum tan - tum Through the town of

Ram - say. Hi did-dle un-kum o - ver the lea, Hi did-dle un-kum fee - dle.

2 The tailor thought his mouse was ill . . .
   He gave him part of a blue pill . . .
      Hi diddle unkum tarum tantum . . .

3 The tailor thought his mouse would die . . .
   He baked him in an apple pie . . .
      Hi diddle unkum tarum tantum . . .

4 The pie was cut, the mouse ran out . . .
   The tailor followed him all about . . .
      Hi diddle unkum tarum tantum . . .

5 The tailor found his mouse was dead . . .
   So he caught another in his stead . . .
      Hi diddle unkum tarum tantum . . .

18 The garden where the praties grow

traditional

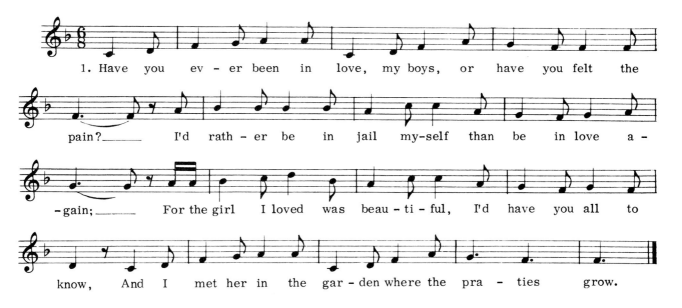

1. Have you ev-er been in love, my boys, or have you felt the pain?____ I'd rath-er be in jail my-self than be in love a-gain;____ For the girl I loved was beau-ti-ful, I'd have you all to know, And I met her in the gar-den where the pra-ties grow.

2   Says I, "My pretty Kathleen, I am tired of single life,
And if you've no objection, sure, I'll make you my sweet wife."
Says she, "I'll ask my parents and tomorrow I'll let you know,
If you'll meet me in the garden where the praties grow."

3   Oh, the parents they consented and we're blessed with children three;
Two girls just like their mother and a boy the image of me.
And now we're going to train them up the way they ought to go,
For to dig out in the garden where the praties grow.

19 The Derby ram

traditional English

1. As I was going to Der-by All on a mar-ket day, ___ I ___ saw the larg-est
lamb, sir, That ev-er was fed ___ on hay. Sing-ing hey ding-le Der-by
Hey ding-le day, Hey ding-le Der-by And hey ding-le day.

2 This ram was fat behind, sir,
This ram was fat before,
This ram was ten yards high, sir,
Indeed he was no more.
    Singing, hey dingle Derby . . .

3 The wool upon his back, sir,
Reached up to the sky,
The eagles built their nests there,
For I heard the young ones cry.
    Singing, hey dingle Derby . . .

4 This ram had four legs to walk upon,
This ram had four legs to stand,
And every leg he had, sir,
Stood on an acre of land.
    Singing, hey dingle Derby . . .

5 The tail upon this ram, sir,
It reached down to hell,
And every time he waggled it
It rang the Devil's bell.
    Singing, hey dingle Derby . . .

6 Now the man that fed the ram, sir,
He fed him twice a day,
And each time that he fed him
He ate a rick of hay.
    Singing, hey dingle Derby . . .

20 Skye boat song

words: Sir Harold Boulton
melody: traditional

"Speed, bonnie boat, like a bird on the wing, On-ward," the sail-ors cry.

"Car – ry the lad that's born to be king O – ver the sea to Skye."

Loud the winds howl, loud the waves roar, Thun – der clouds rend the air;

Baf-fled, our foes stand on the shore, Fol-low they will not dare.

"Speed, bon-nie boat, like a bird on the wing, On-ward," the sail – ors cry.

"Car – ry the lad that's born to be king O – ver the sea to Skye."

21 Scarborough Fair

traditional English

(first tune)

1. "Oh where are you go - ing?" "To Scar - borough

Fair." Seth - er - wood, sale,___ rose - ma - ry and

thyme, "Re - mem - ber me___ to one who lives

there, For once she was___ a true love of mine."

2   "Go tell her to make me a cambric shirt,"
        Setherwood, sale, rosemary and thyme,
    "Without any seam or needle work,
        And then she shall be a true love of mine."

3   "Go tell her to wash it in yonder well,"
     Setherwood, sale, rosemary and thyme,
    "Where never was water nor rain never fell,
      And then she shall be a true love of mine."

4   "Go tell her to dry it on yonder thorn,"
     Setherwood, sale, rosemary and thyme,
    "Which never bore blossom since Adam was born,
      And then she shall be a true love of mine."

5   "Now he has asked me questions three,"
     Setherwood, sale, rosemary and thyme,
    "I hope he will answer as many for me,
      And then he shall be a true love of mine."

6   "Go tell him to find me an acre of land,"
     Setherwood, sale, rosemary and thyme,
    "Betwixt the sea and the sealand side,
      And then he shall be a true love of mine."

7   "Go tell him to plough it with a ram's horn,"
     Setherwood, sale, rosemary and thyme,
    "And sow it all over with one pepper corn,
      And then he shall be a true love of mine."

8   "Go tell him to reap it with a sickle of leather,"
     Setherwood, sale, rosemary and thyme,
    "And bind it up with a peacock's feather,
      And then he shall be a true love of mine."

9   "When he has done and finished his work,"
     Setherwood, sale, rosemary and thyme,
    "Oh, tell him to come and he'll have his shirt,
      And then he shall be a true love of mine."

sale: sallow, a type of willow
setherwood: a plant of the buttercup family
cambric: a type of fine, white linen

Scarborough Fair

traditional

(second tune)

1. "Oh where are you go - ing?" "To Scar - bor - ough

Fair." Seth - er - wood, sale, rose - ma - ry and

thyme, "Re - mem - ber me_____ to one who lives

there, For once she was_____ a true love of mine."

2 "Go tell her to make me a cambric shirt,"
  Setherwood, sale, rosemary and thyme,
 "Without any seam or needle work,
  And then she shall be a true love of mine."

3   "Go tell her to wash it in yonder well,"
      Setherwood, sale, rosemary and thyme,
  "Where never was water nor rain never fell,
     And then she shall be a true love of mine."

4   "Go tell her to dry it on yonder thorn,"
      Setherwood, sale, rosemary and thyme,
  "Which never bore blossom since Adam was born,
     And then she shall be a true love of mine."

5   "Now he has asked me questions three," ·
      Setherwood, sale, rosemary and thyme,
  "I hope he will answer as many for me,
     And then he shall be a true love of mine."

6   "Go tell him to find me an acre of land,"
      Setherwood, sale, rosemary and thyme,
  "Betwixt the sea and the sealand side,
     And then he shall be a true love of mine."

7   "Go tell him to plough it with a ram's horn,"
      Setherwood, sale, rosemary and thyme,
  "And sow it all over with one pepper corn,
     And then he shall be a true love of mine."

8   "Go tell him to reap it with a sickle of leather,"
      Setherwood, sale, rosemary and thyme,
  "And bind it up with a peacock's feather,
     And then he shall be a true love of mine."

9   "When he has done and finished his work,"
      Setherwood, sale, rosemary and thyme,
  "Oh, tell him to come and he'll have his shirt,
     And then he shall be a true love of mine."

sale: sallow, a type of willow
setherwood: a plant of the buttercup family
cambric: a type of fine, white linen

22 The wraggle taggle gipsies

traditional English

1. Three— gip - sies stood at the cast - le gate, They

sang so high, they— sang so low, The la - dy sat in her

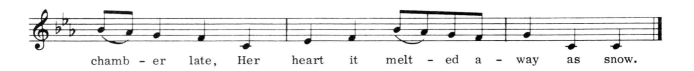

chamb - er late, Her heart it melt - ed a - way as snow.

2 They sang so sweet, they sang so shrill,
   That fast her tears began to flow,
   And she laid down her silken gown,
   Her golden rings and all her show.

3 She pluckèd off her high-heeled shoes,
   A-made of Spanish leather, O.
   She would in the street, with her bare, bare feet,
   All out in the wind and weather, O.

4 It was late last night when my lord came home,
Inquiring for his a-lady, O.
The servants said on ev'ry hand,
"She's gone with the wraggle taggle gipsies, O."

5 "O saddle me my milk-white steed,
And go and fetch me my pony, O.
That I may ride and seek my bride,
Who is gone with the wraggle taggle gipsies, O."

6 O he rode high, and he rode low,
He rode through wood and copses too,
Until he came to an open field,
And there he espied his a-lady, O.

7 "What makes you leave your house and land?
What makes you leave your money, O?
What makes you leave your new-wedded lord,
To follow the wraggle taggle gipsies, O?"

8 "What care I for my house and land?
What care I for my money, O?
What care I for my new-wedded lord?
I'm off with the wraggle taggle gipsies, O."

9 "Last night you slept on a goose-feather bed,
With the sheet turned down so bravely, O.
Tonight you'll sleep in a cold open field,
Along with the wraggle taggle gipsies, O."

10 "What care I for a goose-feather bed,
With the sheet turned down so bravely, O?
Tonight I'll sleep in a cold open field,
Along with the wraggle taggle gipsies, O."

23 William Taylor

traditional English

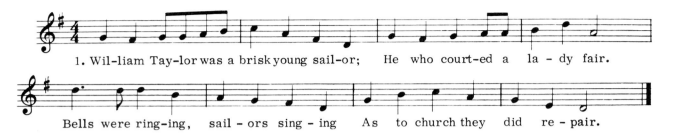

1. Wil-liam Tay-lor was a brisk young sail-or; He who court-ed a la-dy fair.
Bells were ring-ing, sail-ors sing-ing As to church they did re-pair.

2 Thirty couple at the wedding;
All were dressed in rich array.
'Stead of William being married
He was pressed and sent away.

3 She dressed up in man's apparel,
Man's apparel she put on;
And she followed her true lover;
For to find him she is gone.

4 Then the Captain stepped up to her
Asking her, "What's brought you here?"
"I am come to seek my true love,
Who I lately loved so dear."

5 "If you've come to see your true love
Tell me what his name may be."
"Oh, his name is William Taylor,
From the Irish ranks came he."

6 "You rise early tomorrow morning,
You rise at the break of day;
Then you'll see your true love William
Walking with a lady gay."

7 She rose early the very next morning,
She rose up at break of day;
There she saw her true love William
Walking with a lady gay.

8 Sword and pistol she then ordered
To be brought at her command;
And she shot her true love William,
With the bride on his right arm.

9 If young folks in Wells or London
Were served the same as she served he,
Then young girls would all be undone;
Very scarce young men would be!

pressed: forced into the Royal Navy by 'press gangs', whose job it was to recruit young men as sailors

24 Early one morning

traditional English

1. Ear - ly one morn - ing, just as the sun was ris - ing, I
heard a maid - en sing in the val - ley **be** - low.

Chorus
"Oh don't de - ceive me, oh nev - er leave me,
How could you use a poor maid - en so?"

2 "Remember the vows that you made to your Mary,
Remember the day that you vowed to be true.
     Oh don't deceive me, oh never leave me . . ."

3 Thus sang the poor maiden, her sorrows bewailing,
Thus sang the poor maid in the valley below.
     "Oh don't deceive me, oh never leave me . . ."

25 All things are quite silent

traditional English

1. All things are quite si - lent, each mor - tal at rest, When me and my true love got snug in one nest. When a bold set of ruf - fi - ans they ent - ered our cave And forced my dear jew - el to plough the salt wave.

2   I begged for my sailor as I begged for my life.
But they'd not listen to me, although a fond wife,
Saying "The king must have sailors, to sea he must go."
And they've left me lamenting in sorrow and woe.

3   Through green fields and meadows we ofttimes did walk,
And with sweet conversations of love we did talk,
While the birds in the woodland so sweetly did sing,
And the young thrushes' voices made the valleys to ring.

4   Though my love has left me I'll not be cast down.
Who knows but some day my love might return?
And will make me amends for my sorrow and strife,
And me and my true love will be happy for life.

26 The oak and the ash

traditional English

1. A north-country maid up to London had strayed, Although with her nature it did not agree. She— wept and she sighed, and she bitterly cried, "I— wish once again in the north I could be.

Chorus

O the oak, and the ash, and the bonny ivy tree, They— flourish at home in my own country.

2 A maiden I am, and a maiden I'll remain,
Until my own country again I do see,
For here in this place I shall ne'er see the face
Of him that's allotted my love for to be.
    O, the oak, and the ash, and the bonny ivy tree . . .

3 No doubt, did I please, I could marry with ease;
Where maidens are fair many lovers will come.
But he whom I wed must be north-country bred,
And carry me back to my north-country home.
    O, the oak, and the ash, and the bonny ivy tree . . ."

27 The Blue Bell of Scotland

traditional Scottish

1. Oh where, and oh where is your__ High - land lad - die gone? Oh where, and oh where is your__ High - land lad - die gone? He's gone to fight the foe for King__ George up - on the throne, And it's oh, in my heart, I__ wish him safe at home.

2 Oh where, and oh where does your Highland laddie dwell?
Oh where, and oh where does your Highland laddie dwell?
He dwells in merry Scotland at the sign of the Blue Bell,
And it's oh, in my heart, I love my laddie well.

3 Suppose, and suppose that your Highland lad should die?
Suppose, and suppose that your Highland lad should die?
The bagpipes should play o'er him and I'll lay me down and cry,
But it's oh, in my heart, I wish he may not die.

28 Air fa-la-la-lo

traditional

*same tune for verse as chorus

1   There's lilt in the song I sing, there's laughter
      and love,
    There's tang of the sea and blue from heaven above.
    Of reason there's none, and why should there be for bye,
    As long as there's fire in the blood and a light in
      the eye?
        Air fa-la-la-lo ho-ro, air fa-la-la-lay . . .

2   The heather's ablaze with bloom, the myrtle is sweet.
    There's song in the air; the road's a song at our feet.
    So step it along as light as the bird on the wing,
    And, stepping along, let's join our voices and sing
        Air fa-la-la-lo ho-ro, air fa-la-la-lay . . .

3   And whether the blood be highland or lowland or no,
    And whether the skin be black or white as the snow,
    Of kith and of kin we're one, be it right be it wrong,
    As long as our voices join the chorus of song.
        Air fa-la-la-lo ho-ro, air fa-la-la-lay . . .

29 The mermaid

traditional English

1. One___ Fri - day morn when we___ set___ sail, And our ship not far from___ land, We___ there did es-py___ a pret - ty, pret - ty maid, With a comb and a glass___ in her hand, her hand, her hand, With a comb and a glass in her hand.

Chorus

While the ra - ging seas___ did___ roar, And the storm - y winds did___ blow, And___ we jol - ly sail - or boys were

up, were up a-loft, And the land - lub-bers ly - ing down be -

low, be-low, be-low, And the land lub-bers ly - ing down be - low.

2 And then up spoke the captain of our ship,
Who at once our peril did see.
"I have married a wife in fair London town,
And tonight she a widow will be, will be,
    will be,
And tonight she a widow will be."
        While the raging seas did roar . . .

3 And then up spoke the little cabin boy,
And a fair-haired boy was he.
"I've a father and mother in fair Portsmouth town,
And tonight they will weep for me, for me,
    for me,
And tonight they will weep for me."
        While the raging seas did roar . . .

4 Then three times round went our gallant ship,
And three times round went she,
Then three times round went our gallant,
    gallant ship,
And she sank to the bottom of the sea, the sea,
    the sea,
And she sank to the bottom of the sea.
        While the raging seas did roar . . .

glass: mirror

30 Danny Boy

words: Fred. E. Weatherly
melody: traditional Irish (Londonderry Air)

Introduction Verse

1. Oh, Dan-ny Boy, the pipes, the pipes are
2. But when you come, and all the flow'rs are

call - ing From glen to glen and down the mountain - side. The summer's
dy - ing, If I am dead, as dead I may well be, You'll come and

gone, and all the ro-ses fall - ing, It's you, it's you must go and I must
find the place where I am ly - ing, And kneel and say an A - ve there for

bide. But come you back when summer's in the mead - ow, Or when the
me; And I shall hear, though soft you tread a - bove me, And all my

val - ley's hushed and white with snow. It's I'll be there in sun-shine or in
grave will warm-er, sweet-er be, For you will bend and tell me that you

sha - dow. Oh, Dan-ny Boy, oh Dan-ny Boy I love you so.
love me, And I shall sleep in peace un - til you come to me.

31 Blow the man down

traditional (capstan shanty)

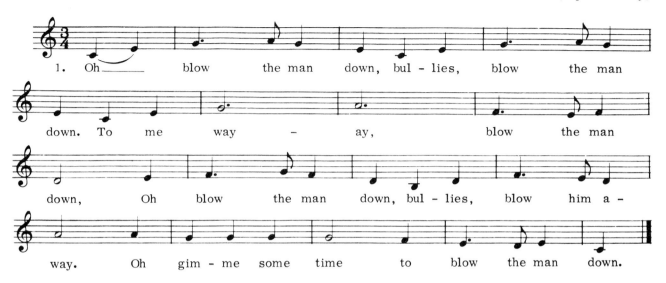

1. Oh_____ blow the man down, bul – lies, blow the man down. To me way – ay, blow the man down, Oh blow the man down, bul – lies, blow him a – way. Oh gim – me some time to blow the man down.

2 We went over the Bar on the thirteenth of May . . .
   The Galloper jumped, and the gale came away . . .

3 Oh the rags they were gone, and the chains they was jammed . . .
   And the skipper sez he, "Let the weather be hanged . . ."

4 Oh it's sailors is tinkers, and tailors is men . . .
   And we're all of us coming to see you again . . .

5 So we'll blow the man up, and we'll blow the man down . . .
   And we'll blow him away into Liverpool town . . .

blow: strike, knock
bar: a bank of sand, or silt, across the mouth of a river or harbour which obstructs navigation

32 My bonnie lies over the ocean

traditional English

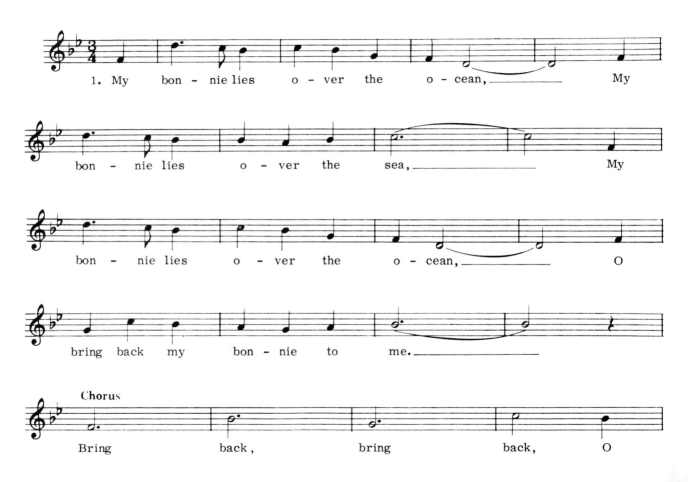

1. My bon - nie lies o - ver the o - cean,_____ My
bon - nie lies o - ver the sea,_____ My
bon - nie lies o - ver the o - cean,_____ O
bring back my bon - nie to me._____

Chorus

Bring back, bring back, O

bring back my bon - nie to me, to me.

Bring back, bring back, O

bring back my bon - nie to me.

2 Last night as I lay on my pillow
   Last night as I lay on my bed,
   Last night as I lay on my pillow,
   I dreamed that my bonnie was dead.
      Bring back, bring back . . .

3 O blow ye winds over the ocean,
   O blow ye winds over the sea,
   O blow ye winds over the ocean,
   And bring back my bonnie to me.
      Bring back, bring back . . .

4 The winds have blown over the ocean,
   The winds have blown over the sea,
   The winds have blown over the ocean,
   And brought back my bonnie to me.
      Bring back, bring back . . .

33 Spanish Ladies

traditional English

1. Fare - well and a - dieu un-to you, Span-ish La - dies, Fare - well and a - dieu to you, La - dies of Spain. For_ we've re - ceived or - ders to_ sail for old Eng - land; But we hope in a short time to see you a - gain.

Chorus

We'll rant and we'll rove like_ true Brit - ish sail - ors. We'll rant and we'll rove o'er_ all the salt seas, Un - til we strike sound - ings in the Chan-nel of Old

Eng - land. From Ush - ant to Scil - ly is thir - ty five leagues.

2 We hove our ship to, with the wind at sou'west, boys,
   We hove our ship to; for to strike soundings clear.
   Then filled the main tops'l and bore right away, boys,
   And straight up the Channel our course we did steer.
       We'll rant and we'll rove like true British sailors . . .

3 The first land we made, it is known as the Deadman.
   Then Ram Head, off Plymouth, Start, Portland and Wight.
   We sailed then by Beachy, by Fairlee and Dungeness,
   Until we came abreast of the South Foreland light.
       We'll rant and we'll rove like true British sailors . . .

4 Then signal was made for the Grand Fleet to anchor,
   For all in the Downs that night were to meet.
   'Twas, "Stand by your stoppers! Let go your shank painters!
   Haul up your clew garnets! Stick out tack and sheets!"
       We'll rant and we'll rove like true British sailors . . .

5 Now let every man toss off a full bumper,
   Let every man toss off a full bowl.
   And we'll drink and be merry and drown melancholy,
   Singing, "Here's a good health to all true-hearted souls!"
       We'll rant and we'll rove like true British sailors . . .

soundings: a place in the English Channel
     where it is possible to reach the bottom
     with an ordinary deep sea lead
hove: wait
league: three nautical miles
stopper: a short piece of rope
shank-painter: the rope with which the
     ship's anchor is attached to the side
clew-garnet: a tackle to guide the sails
tack, sheet: ropes attached to the sails and
     used to alter the ship's direction
haul: to trim the sails so as to sail nearer
     the wind

34 Rio Grande

traditional

1. I'll   sing   you   a   song   of   the   fish   in   the   sea.

Oh, _____ Ri - o! _____ I'll   sing   you   a   song   of   the

fish   in   the   sea. And   we're   bound   for   the   Ri - o   Grande.   Then   a -

Chorus

way,   love __ a - way;   'way _____ down   Ri - o! _____ So

fare __ you   well __ my   pret - ty   young   girl   For   we're   bound   for   the   Ri - o   Grande. _____

2 We've a ship that is strong and a jolly good crew,
    Oh, Rio!
A brass-knuckled mate and a rough skipper too.
And we're bound for the Rio Grande.
    Then away, love, away; 'way down Rio . . .

3 So it's pack up your donkey and get under way.
    Oh, Rio!
The girls we are leaving can take our half pay.
And we're bound for the Rio Grande.
    Then away, love, away; 'way down Rio . . .

4 Sing goodbye to Sally and goodbye to Sue,
    Oh, Rio!
And you who are listening, goodbye to you.
And we're bound for the Rio Grande.
    Then away, love, away; 'way down Rio . . .

35 Bushes and briars

traditional English

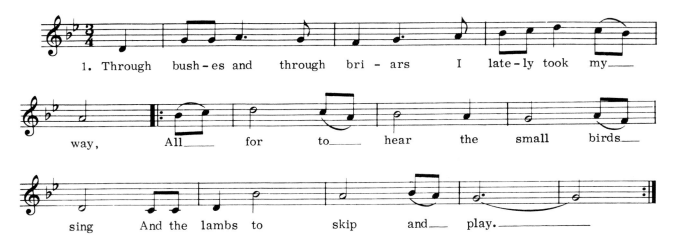

1. Through bush-es and through bri-ars I late-ly took my way, All for to hear the small birds sing And the lambs to skip and play.

2 I overheard my own true love,
  Her voice it was so clear:
  Long time have I been waiting for
  The coming of my dear,
  Long time have I been waiting for
  The coming of my dear.

3 Sometimes I am uneasy
  And troubled in my mind,
  Sometimes I think I'll go to my love
  And tell him all my mind,
  Sometimes I think I'll go to my love
  And tell him all my mind.

4 And if I should go to my love,
  My love he will say nay,
  If I show to him my boldness
  He'll ne'er love me again,
  If I show to him my boldness
  He'll ne'er love me again.

36 Windy old weather

traditional

Chorus

1. As we were a-fishing off Haisborough light, Shooting and hauling and trawling all night, It was

win-dy old weather, storm-y old weath-er, When the wind blows, we all pull to-geth-er.

2　We sighted a herring, the king of the sea,
　　Says, "Now, old skipper, you cannot catch me."
　　　　It was windy old weather, stormy old weather . . .

3　We sighted a mackerel with stripes on his back.
　　"Time now, old skipper, to shift your main tack."
　　　　It was windy old weather, stormy old weather . . .

4　We sighted a conger as long as a mile.
　　"Wind's blowing easterly," he said with a smile.
　　　　It was windy old weather, stormy old weather . . .

5　We sighted a plaice that had spots on his side.
　　Says, "Now, old skipper, these seas you won't ride."
　　　　It was windy old weather, stormy old weather . . .

6　I think what these fishes are saying is right.
　　We'll haul in our nets and we'll make for the light.
　　　　It was windy old weather, stormy old weather . . .

tack: a rope used to secure the corners of the lower square-sails to the ship's side

37 There's a big ship sailing

traditional

1. There's a big ship sail - ing on the il - ly-al - ly - o, The il - ly-al - ly - o, the il - ly-al - ly - o, There's a big ship sail - ing on the il - ly-al - ly - o, Heigh - ho, il - ly-al - ly - o.

2 There's a big ship sailing, rocking on the sea,
Rocking on the sea, rocking on the sea,
There's a big ship sailing, rocking on the sea,
Heigh-ho, rocking on the sea.

3 The Captain said, "It'll never, never do,
Never, never do, never, never do."
The Captain said, "It'll never, never do,
Heigh-ho, never, never do."

4 The big ship sank to the bottom of the sea,
The bottom of the sea, the bottom of the sea,
The big ship sank to the bottom of the sea,
Heigh-ho, the bottom of the sea.

illy-ally-o: sea

38 Donkey riding

traditional (capstan shanty)

1. Were you ev-er in Lon-don town, Where the girls they do come down

To see the King in a gold-en crown Rid-ing on a don-key?

Chorus

Hey, ho, a-way we go, Don-key rid-ing, don-key rid-ing,

Hey, ho, a-way we go, Rid-ing on a don-key.

2 Were you ever off Cape Horn,
   Where it's always fine and warm,
   And seen the lion and the unicorn
      Riding on a donkey?
         Hey, ho, away we go . . .

3 Were you ever in Cardiff Bay,
   Where the folks all shout, "Hurray!
   Here comes John with his three years pay
      Riding on a donkey?"
         Hey, ho, away we go . . .

39 Green grow the rushes, ho!

traditional English

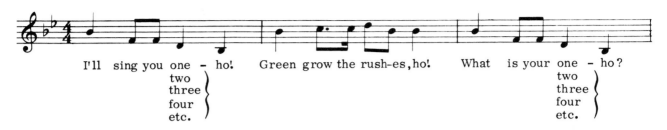

I'll sing you one - ho! Green grow the rush-es, ho! What is your one - ho?
two
three
four
etc.
two
three
four
etc.

Verse 1 only

One is one and all a - lone and ev - er more shall be so.

②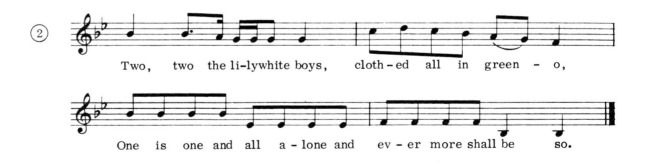

Two, two the li-lywhite boys, cloth - ed all in green - o,

One is one and all a - lone and ev - er more shall be so.

③

Three, three the ri - vals, ⟶ ②

④ Four for the Gos-pel mak - ers, ⟶ ③

⑤ Five for the sym-bols at your door and
⑥ Six for the six proud walk - ers, ____

Four for the Gos-pel mak - ers, ⟶ ③

⑦ Seven for the seven stars in the sky and
⑧ Eight for the A - pril rain - ers, ____
⑨ Nine for the nine bright shin - ers, ____
⑩ Ten for the ten com-mand - ments, __

Six for the six proud walk - ers, ⟶ ⑤

⑪ Eleven for the eleven went up to heav'n, and
⑫ Twelve for the twelve A - post - les, _____

Ten for the ten com - mand - ments, ⟶ ⑨

40 The drummer and the cook

traditional
(capstan shanty)

1. Oh there was a lit-tle drummer And he loved a one-eyed cook. And he

Chorus

loved her, oh he loved her Though she had a cock-eyed look, With her

one eye in the pot. And the oth-er up the chim-ney. With a

bow-wow-wow, Fal-lal the dow-a-did-dy Bow-wow-wow.

2 When this couple went a-courtin'
   For to walk along the shore,
   Sez the drummer to the cookie,
   "You're the girl that I adore."
      With her one eye in the pot . . .

3 When this couple went a-courtin'
   For to walk along the pier,
   Sez the cookie to the drummer,
   "An' I love you too, my dear."
      With her one eye in the pot . . .

4 Sez the drummer to the cookie,
"Ain't the weather fine today?"
Sez the cookie to the drummer,
"Is that all ye got to say?"
    With her one eye in the pot . . .

5 Sez the drummer to the cookie,
"Will I buy the weddin' ring?"
Sez the cookie, "Now you're talkin'.
That would be the very thing."
    With her one eye in the pot . . .

6 Sez the drummer to the cookie,
"Will ye name the weddin' day?"
Sez the cookie, "We'll be married
In the merry month o' May."
    With her one eye in the pot . . .

7 When they went to church to say
"I will," the drummer got a nark,
For her one eye gliffed the Parson
And the other killed the clerk.
    With her one eye in the pot . . .

gliffed: frightened
nark: a disagreeable surprise
caused by a person and not by
a circumstance

41 Golden slumbers

17th century English

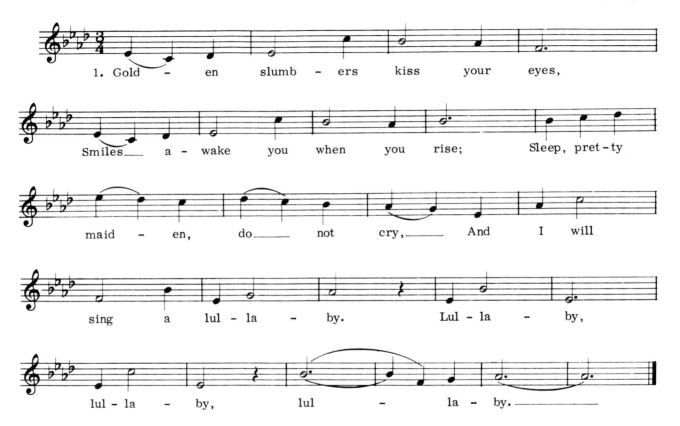

1. Gold - en slumb - ers kiss your eyes,
Smiles— a - wake you when you rise; Sleep, pret - ty
maid - en, do— not cry,— And I will
sing a lul - la - by. Lul - la - by,
lul - la - by, lul - la - by.—

2 Care you know not, therefore sleep
While I o'er you watch do keep;
Sleep, pretty darling, do not cry,
And I will sing a lullaby.
Lullaby, lullaby, lullaby.

42 Paper of pins

traditional

I'll give to you a pa-per of pins, If that's the way that love be-gins, If you will mar-ry, marry, marry, marry, If you'll mar-ry me.

2 I don't want your paper of pins,
  If that's the way that love begins,
  For I won't marry, marry, marry, marry,
  I won't marry you.

3 I'll give to you a dress of red
  Stitched all around with golden thread
  If you will marry, marry, marry, marry,
  If you'll marry me.

4 I don't want your dress of red
  Stitched all around with golden thread
  For I won't marry, marry, marry, marry,
  I won't marry you.

5 I'll give to you the key to my chest
  And all the money that I possess
  If you will marry, marry, marry, marry,
  If you'll marry me.

6 Yes, I'll accept the key to your chest
  And all the money that you possess.
  Yes, I will marry, marry, marry, marry,
  I will marry you.

7 Ah, ha, ha, money is all
  A woman's love is nothing at all.
  No, I'll not marry, marry, marry, marry,
  I'll not marry you.

43 Sweet Polly Oliver

traditional English

1. As sweet Pol - ly Ol - i - ver lay mus - ing in bed, A sud - den strange fan - cy came in - to her head; "Nor fa - ther nor mo - ther shall make me false prove! I'll 'list for a sol - dier and fol - low my love."

2 So early next morning she softly arose,
   And dressed herself up in her dead brother's clothes;
   She cut her hair close and she stained her face brown,
   And went for a soldier to fair London town.

3   Then up spake the sergeant one day at his drill;
      "Now who's good for nursing? A Captain lies ill."
      "I'm ready," says Polly: to nurse him she's gone,
      And finds 'tis her true love all wasted and wan.

4   The first week the doctor kept shaking his head:
      "No nursing, young fellow, can save him," he said.
      But when Polly Oliver had nursed back his life,
      He cried "You have cherished him as if you were his wife!"

5   Oh then Polly Oliver she burst into tears,
      And told the good doctor her hopes and her fears;
      And very soon after, for better for worse,
      The Captain took joyfully his pretty soldier nurse.

44 Blow away the morning dew

words: traditional English
melody: traditional Irish

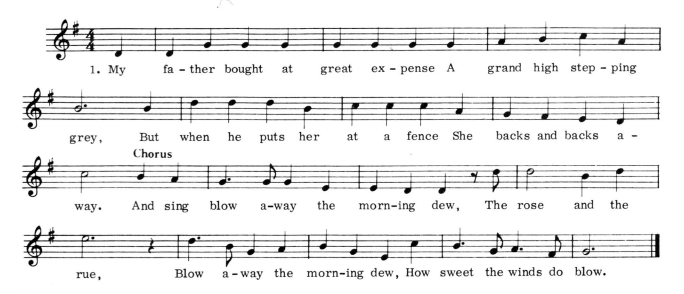

1. My father bought at great expense A grand high stepping grey, But when he puts her at a fence She backs and backs away.

Chorus

And sing blow away the morning dew, The rose and the rue, Blow away the morning dew, How sweet the winds do blow.

2 My mother bought a likely hen
On last St Martin's day;
She clucks and clucks and clucks again
But never yet will lay.
     And sing blow away the morning dew . . .

3 Oh Mustard is my brother's dog
Who whines and wags his tail,
And snuffs into the market bag
But dare not snatch the meal.
     And sing blow away the morning dew . . .

4 When walls lie down for steeds to step,
When eggs themselves go lay,
And the groats jump into Mustard's jaws,
To you my court I'll pay.
     And sing blow away the morning dew . . .

groat: coarse oatmeal

45 Suo-gân

traditional Welsh

1. Sleep, my ba - by, rest, my loved one, Soft - ly slum-ber now with me,

Clasped in moth-er's arms so ten - der, Warm in moth-er's love for thee.

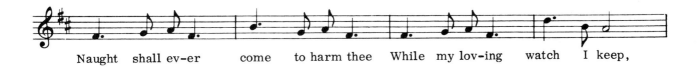

Naught shall ev-er come to harm thee While my lov-ing watch I keep,

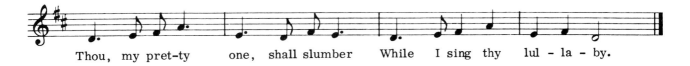

Thou, my pret-ty one, shall slumber While I sing thy lul - la - by.

2 Sleep, my baby, rest, my loved one,
While the evening shadows creep.
Why, my dearest, art thou smiling,
Smiling sweetly in thy sleep?
Can it be that all the angels
In God's Heaven smile on thee?
Rest, my darling, smile and slumber
While I sing thy lullaby.

46 O can ye sew cushions?

Scottish lullaby

1. O can ye sew cu-shions, and can ye sew sheets, And

can you sing＿ ba - la-loo when my bon-nie greets? And＿

hee and baw bird - ie, and＿ hee and baw lamb, And

hee and baw bird - ie my bon - nie wee lamb.

Chorus

Hee - o, haw - o, what'll I do with you? Black's the life that I lead with you.

Ma - ny of you; lit-tle to give you, Hee - o, haw - o, what'll I do with you?

2   Now hush-a-by lammie, and hush-a-by dear,
    Now hush-a-by lammie, your mother is here.
    The wild wind is raving, your mother's heart's sore,
    The wild wind is raving, but you care no more.
        Hee-o, haw-o, what'll I do with you? . . .

3   Sing balaloo lammie, sing balaloo dear,
    Does wee lammie know that its daddy's not here?
    You're rocking quite sweetly on mother's warm knee,
    But daddy's a-rocking upon the salt sea.
        Hee-o, haw-o, what'll I do with you? . . .

47 Barbara Allen (first tune)

traditional (English song)

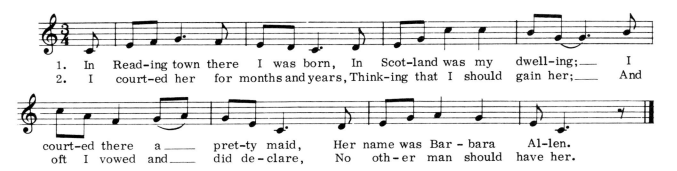

1. In Read-ing town there I was born, In Scot-land was my dwell-ing;— I
   court-ed there a——— pret-ty maid, Her name was Bar - bara Al-len.

2. I court-ed her for months and years, Think-ing that I should gain her;— And
   oft I vowed and——— did de-clare, No oth-er man should have her.

3 I sent a man to yonder town,
To ask for Barbara Allen;
"You must come to my master's house,
If you be Barbara Allen."

4 So slowly she put on her clothes,
So slowly she came to him;
And when she came to his bedside,
"Young man," she said "You're dying."

5 He turned his face unto the wall
And death came slowly to him,
"Adieu, adieu to all my friends,
Farewell to Barbara Allen."

6 And as she walked across the field
And heard his death bell tolling,
And every toll, it seemed to say,
"Hard hearted Barbara Allen."

7 "Oh mother dear, make me my bed,
And make it for my sorrow.
A young man died for me today,
I'll die for him tomorrow."

8 So he did die on one good day,
And she died on the morrow,
Oh, he did die for love of her,
And she did die for sorrow.

(second tune)

traditional (Scottish air)

1. In Read-ing town there I was born, In Scot-land was my dwell-ing; I court-ed there a pret-ty maid, Her name was Bar-bara Al-len. 2. I court-ed her for months and years, Think-ing that I should gain her; And oft I vowed and did de-clare, No oth-er man should have her.

48 Mush, mush

1. Oh 'twas there I learned read - in' an' writ - in',
   me we 'ad man - y a scrim - mage,

At Bil - ly Brack - ett's where I went to school,
An' dev - il a cop - y I wrote.

An' 'twas there I learned 'ow - lin' an' fight - in'
There was ne'er a gos - soon in the vil - lage

With me school - mas - ter Mist - er O' - Toole.
Dared tread on the tail o' me

'Im an'

Chorus

Mush, mush, mush tu - ral - i - ad - dy,

Sing mush, mush, mush tur - al - i - ay.

There was ne'er a gos - soon in the vil - lage

Dared tread on the tail o' me coat. _____

2 Oh 'twas there that I learned all me courtin',
Oh the lessons I took in the art,
Till Cupid, the blackguard, while sportin',
An arrow drove straight through me heart.
Judy O'Connor she lived just near me
An' tender lines to her I wrote.
If ye dare say one hard word against her
I'll tread on the tail o' your
    Mush, mush, mush tural-i-addy . . .

3 But a blackguard called Micky Maloney
Came an' stole her affections away
For he'd money, an' I hadn't any,
So I sent him a challenge next day.
In the evenin' we met at the Woodbine,
The Shannon we crossed in a boat,
An' I lathered 'im with me shillaly
For he trod on the tail o' me
    Mush, mush, mush tural-i-addy . . .

4 Oh me fame went abroad through the nation,
An' folks came a-flockin' to see,
An' they cried out without hesitation
"You're a fightin' man Billy McGee."
Oh I've cleaned out the Finnigan faction
An' I've licked all the Murphies afloat,
If you're in for a fight or a ruction,
Just tread on the tail o' me
    Mush, mush, mush tural-i-addy . . .

gossoon: lad
scrimmage: scuffle
shillally: shillelagh, an Irish cudgel of blackthorn or oak

49 The tree in the wood

traditional English

1. All in a wood there grew a tree, The fi - nest tree you ev - er did see, And the green leaves grew a - round, a-round, a-round, And the green leaves grew a - round. 2. And on this tree there was a limb, The fin - est limb you ev - er did see, The limb was on the tree, The tree was in the wood, And the green leaves grew a - round, a-round, a-round, And the green leaves grew a - round. 3. And round.

*this bar repeated as necessary

3 And on this limb there was a branch,
  The finest branch you ever did see, *(to 3 opposite)*

4 And on this branch there was a nest,
  The finest nest you ever did see, *(to 4)*

5 And in this nest there was an egg,
  The finest egg you ever did see, *(to 5)*

6 And in this egg there was a yolk,
  The finest yolk you ever did see, *(to 6)*

7 And in this yolk there was a bird,
  The finest bird you ever did see, *(to 7)*

8 And on this bird there was a wing,
  The finest wing you ever did see, *(to 8)*

9 And on this wing there was a feather,
  The finest feather you ever did see, *(to 9)*

9 The feather was on the wing,
8 The wing was on the bird,
7 The bird was in the yolk,
6 The yolk was in the egg
5 The egg was in the nest,
4 The nest was on the branch,
3 The branch was on the limb,
2 The limb was on the tree,
1 The tree was in the wood,
  And the green leaves grew around,
      around, around,
  And the green leaves grew around.

50 Widdicombe Fair

traditional English

1. Tom Pearce, Tom Pearce lend me your gray mare, All a-long, down a-long,

out a-long lee. For I want for to go ___ to Wid - di-combe Fair With Bill

Chorus

Brew-er, Jan Stew-er, Pe-ter Gurn-ey, Pe-ter Da-vy, Dan'l Whid-don, Har-ry Hawk, Old

Unc - le Tom Cobbleigh and all, ___ Old Unc - le Tom Cobbleigh and all. ___

2 And when shall I see again my gray mare?
     All along, down along, out along lee.
   By Friday soon, or Saturday noon,
        With Bill Brewer, Jan Stewer . . .

3 So they harnessed and bridled the old gray mare,
     All along, down along, out along lee.
   And off they drove to Widdicombe Fair,
        With Bill Brewer, Jan Stewer . . .

4   Then Friday came and Saturday noon,
      All along, down along, out along lee.
    But Tom Pearce's old mare have not trotted home,
      With Bill Brewer, Jan Stewer . . .

5   So Tom Pearce he got up to the top of the hill,
      All along, down along, out along lee.
    And he seed his old mare down a-making her will,
      With Bill Brewer, Jan Stewer . . .

6   So Tom Pearce's old mare her took sick and died,
      All along, down along, out along lee.
    And Tom he sat down on a stone and he cried,
      With Bill Brewer, Jan Stewer . . .

7   But this isn't the end of this shocking affair,
      All along, down along, out along lee.
    Nor, though they be dead, of the horrid career,
      With Bill Brewer, Jan Stewer . . .

8   When the wind whistles cold on the moor of a night,
      All along, down along, out along lee.
    Tom Pearce's old mare does appear ghastly white
      With Bill Brewer, Jan Stewer . . .

9   And all the night long be heard skirling and groans,
      All along, down along, out along lee.
    From Tom Pearce's old mare and a rattling of bones,
      With Bill Brewer, Jan Stewer . . .

skirling: shrill crying or shrieking

51 Johnny Todd

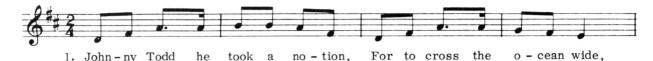

1. John-ny Todd he took a no-tion, For to cross the o-cean wide,

And he left his love be-hind him Weep-ing by the Li-ver-pool tide.

2 For a week she wept full sorely,
Tore her hair and wrung her hands,
Then she met another sailor
Walking on the Liverpool sands.

3 "Why fair maid are you a-weeping
For your Johnny gone to sea?
If you'll wed with me tomorrow,
I will kind and constant be.

4 I will buy you sheets and blankets
I'll buy you a wedding ring,
You will have a silver cradle,
For to rock your babies in."

5 Johnny Todd came home from sailing,
Sailing o'er the ocean wide
For to find his fair and false one
Was another sailor's bride.

6 All young men who go a-sailing,
For to fight the foreign foe,
Never leave your love, like Johnny,
Marry her before you go.

Acknowledgements

The publishers would like to thank Sue Wesselman and Vic Whitburn for their help in compiling this book.

The following copyright owners have kindly granted their permission for the reprinting of words and music:

Cramer Music for the words of 21 "Skye boat song".

J. Curwen & Sons Ltd for 8 "Billy Boy", from *The Shanty Book* (Curwen Edition 2591/52), collected and edited by Sir R.R. Terry.

Novello and Company Ltd for 35 "Bushes and briars", collected by R. Vaughan Williams, and for 23 "William Taylor" and 33 "Spanish Ladies", collected by Cecil J. Sharp.

Stainer & Bell for 5 "Spinning Wheel Song". This song is from *Fairy Isle: a garland of Manx Folk Songs* by Arnold Foster, and is available separately as part of the Stainer & Bell song series.

Mrs Ursula Vaughan Williams for 25 "All things are quite silent".

Every effort has been made to trace and acknowledge copyright owners. If any right has been omitted, the publishers offer their apologies and will rectify this in subsequent editions following notification.

Index of first lines